Verse for the Earth
More Green Poems for a Blue Planet

Proud to be partnered with Bristol, European Green Capital 2015.
www.bristol2015.co.uk

To greenies, non-greenies and inbetweenies everywhere!

Verse for the Earth
More Green Poems for a Blue Planet

Martin Kiszko

Illustrations by Nick Park

Wild Idea

Green Gratitude

Thanks to all the 'poo powered' fans out there who bought the first book and came to the show and workshops. Glad you liked! Accolades of appreciation to Simon Bishop for the book's design and layout. A thousand thanks to Jacki Hill-Murphy for editing the early drafts and to Margaret Burden and Duncan Wright for proofreading the later ones. Grateful green thanks to producer Adam Glen for joining in on the green poems adventures plus a big thank you note to Lee Walters for website management. A doff of the hat to Richard Jones for his publishing wisdom and ta very much to Chris Jones at *Otrovez* for waving his magic marketing wand. Most of all, tributes to the individuals, organisations, and business poem sponsors who had the vision and commitment to support this book and contribute to building a greener future.

Martin Kiszko

First published in 2014 by Wild Idea Ltd.

Contact
Web: www.greenpoemsforablueplanet.com
E: contact@greenpoemsforablueplanet.com
You Tube: http://www.youtube.com/watch?v=i-zCZC_JgzA
FB: www.facebook.com/home.php?#!/pages/green-poems-for-a-blue-planet/132291276782066
Twitter: @martinkiszko

ISBN: 978-0-9568549-1-9

British Library Cataloguing-in-Publications Data:
A Catalogue record for this book is available from The British Library.

Cover illustration by Nick Park; cover and book design by Simon Bishop.
Printed in the Czech Republic via Akcent Media.

FSC
www.fsc.org
MIX
Paper from
responsible sources
FSC® C014138

Contents

Green Teen

I'm the greenest teenager I know
With green nail polished fingers and toes.
In the loos at lunchtime I spray tan my skin lime,
And there's plenty of green up my nose.

My eyelashes are olive and fake,
And I wear my jade earrings at break.
My fluorescent extensions got me in detention,
How much can a 'greenager' take?

What am I expected to do
If the school uniform's blue?
Guess they'll send home a letter about my green sweater
Not being the regular hue.

What's so wrong with letting me show
My personal take on 'eco'?
Don't they *get* what I *mean* about *being green*?
I'm the greenest teenager I know!

For Luke and Vita Wilkinson.

If I Had to Choose a Car

In LA, London, Kandahar,
Mums, dads, grandmas, grandpapas,
Whether poor or superstars,
Are talking about the greenest car.

In Detroit, Frankfurt and Geneva,
There's eco-auto tweeting fever.
The cleanest leanest meanest car
Has tyremarked social media.

'What is this car?' I hear you say.
Would you like the exposé?
The buzz is stop-start fuel consumption,
Lithium ion battery function,
Brake energy regeneration,
Aerodynamic calibration.
The engine runs on rotten eggs,
Tea and cappuccino dregs.
Bumpers are two bales of hay,
The spec says that it's foldaway.

The dashboard features deer detection
And badger warning light protection.
Cat Sat Nav is in the deal,
No more meows beneath the wheels!
Even hedgehogs, hares and toads
Are lining up along the roads.
They've read in *Which Green Car is That?*
About the frog-hog anti-splat!

Also included in the price:
The 'save a pheasant' scan device.
For any wildlife hitch or glitch,
Flick the 'pelt prevention' switch.

So, from all the hoo and all the ha,
The tweets, the posts, the blogs and blah,
I'd say this model's best by far
If I had to choose a car.

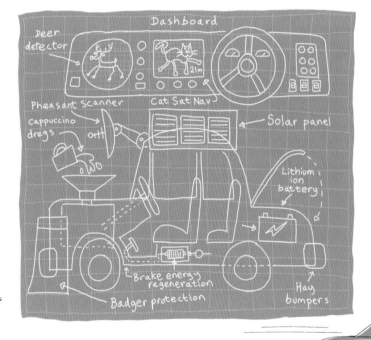

Poem sponsor: **Shirani Le Mercier**, Producer.
www.springtimefilms.com

For Manoli and Ela.

Bin Twister

Blue bin,	green bin,	brown bin,	black bin,
Green bin,	blue bin,	black bin,	brown bin,
Black bin,	brown bin,	green bin,	blue bin,
Brown bin,	black bin,	blue bin,	green bin.

Try this tongue twister. How quickly can you say it? Can you repeat it while sorting the rubbish into your bins?

Try it with the colours changed on the words. Is it easier or harder?

Bin Twister Twisted!

Blue bin,   green bin,   brown bin,   black bin,
Green bin,   blue bin,   black bin,   brown bin,
Black bin,   brown bin,   green bin,   blue bin,
Brown bin,   black bin,   blue bin,   green bin.

Poem sponsor:

The Pitch Project
Pitch it ● Green it ● Film it ● Take it to Hollywood
www.enterthepitch.com

What You've Got

You could go out and buy a lot
At a megastore or shop,
From a site on the Net
Or a catalogue you get.
I've no idea what you'd choose
Amongst the items to peruse.
You might check out computer games,
Something trendy for your room,
Slim laptop with the latest spec,
A gadget here - a gadget there,
Three outfits you can't wait to wear,
Perhaps a pair of running shoes,
A smartphone, skateboard or a bike,
Loads of music that you like,
Attractive junk and gorgeous tat,
A plastic this, a plastic that,
Sold as a trinket or a fad,
Something that will entertain:
Gold or silver on a chain.
Of course it's cool to buy brand new,
And go for many not for few,
Then dash to a department store,
And purchase more from every floor.
You certainly must buy a bag
To carry all the stuff you have.
When you've left the shopping zone
With all that money quickly blown,
And all you've bought is now back home,
Sit down and chill with what you own.
You could go out and buy a lot
Or you could stick with what you've got!

Poem sponsor: Proud to be partnered with **Bristol, European Green Capital 2015**.
www.bristol2015.co.uk

The Case of the Murdered Mahogany

A forest floor of shade and moss.
A patrol car pulls up at the spot.
The detective climbs out from the rear,
Surveys the site, 'What have we here?'

The crime scene was securely fenced
Protecting any evidence
The suspect might have left behind
For a super-sleuth to find.

The investigator caught his breath,
'Such a tragic eco death.'
He stared at what was once a tree,
'Another murdered mahogany.'

The Coroner took a look around,
Gave her report on what she found:
'Sawn to a stump. Life-sap gone.'
She pronounced, 'tree dead at half past one.

It's murder in the first degree
Of a defenceless mahogany,
Shown no mercy that's a fact,
And couldn't flee the criminal's act.'

The forensic team was standing by
With cameras and beady eyes.
Dressed in latex gloves and suits,
They searched the ground and traced the roots.

'We've found stray branches stripped and hacked.
The weapons used: chain-saws and axe.
Tracks show the trunk was hauled through mud.
Here's where they loaded up the wood.

This tree is just another number
Slaughtered for its precious lumber.
Illegally sold for dirty money,
The once stood proud mahogany.'

The detective made a note or two,
'A mahogicide. It's up to you
To follow every lead, print, clue,
And find the trail to why and who.

I'm sure that those who planned this crime
Will return another time.
It won't be long before we'll see
More murdered mahoganies.'

Living on the Edge Hog

I'm living on the edge,
I'm an on the edge hog,
Looking for a home
In a random pile of logs.
And where's the hedge gone
That was once around this field?
I used to go hang out there
For an insect snack or meal.
What about the garden
That used to have my nest?
It's now garages and carports,
I'm so not impressed.
The only chance I get round here
Is to roll into a ball
And roll away from everything,
I can't take it all...
...since
My dad's a 2D hedgehog
Squashed by a four by four.
My mum she ate a poisoned slug
And now she is no more.

My brother found his way back home
Fenced off by wood and wire.
My sister's place is ashes,
Gone in a garden fire.
My uncle he is flatmeat,
My aunt's a tarmac stain,
My cousin's under concrete,
My mate drowned in a drain.

And me? I'm on a precipice,
I'm running out of time.
It's like walking on a tightrope,
My life is on the line.
Okay I can be spiky,
But I'm spiked up with emotion.
We'll all be gone in twenty years
Without some hog devotion.

I'm a nervy, edgy, hedgehog
Living on the edge.
I'm an on the edge hog
Who'd be better in a hedge! ☺

Poem sponsor: **PJ Crook**, Artist. www.pjcrook.com

slick

Could
someone
be
taking
the mick?
The black goo on my toes is toxic.
Are my sunglasses' lenses that thick? Or are the beaches all buried in slick?
My watch simply counts the tick ticks
As the spill grows cataclysmic.
From my flip-flops to the Atlantic
Everything's covered in slick.
They've sure got a problem to lick as they drown fish in slithery slick.
Pelican feathers stick, stick, and my sun-bed is full of oiled chicks.
Are their brains as thick as a brick?
They should have been quickety quick.
It takes more than a few techie tricks
To cap millions of gallons of slick.
They tried to be slickety slick
Making money from running a rig.
Profits versus clean sand - take your pick -
Polluting the ocean is sick.
Got my laptop to clickety-click
Petroleum giants with big e-mail kicks.
They'll get my black cross not a tick.
Making
a
slick
isn't
slick.

Bird Table

The table top was set for eight,
The guests due at the stroke of nine,
An hour on, the clock struck ten,
Not one guest had arrived by then.

The host and hostess checked the time,
'It's odd the cuckoo's not here first,
He usually grabs the main guest's seat,
No sign of him. I fear the worst.'

The host watched from the front door mat.
'So strange - the wagtail's never late.'
The hostess drew the curtains back.
'And the starling never missed a date.'

'Perhaps the sparrow double booked,
Or her flight was extra long?
And what about the nightingale?
He would have called with chirp and song.'

'The skylark promised she'd be here.
I guess no-one would mind her chicks.
The woodcock's time is night-life based,
I bet he's gone downtown for kicks.'

'That fashionista willow tit
What more to say? Has let us down.
She asked about the dress code twice,
Could she have soiled her feathered gown?'

So no-one knocked,
And no one came.
Not only were they very late,
No bird invited kept the date.
In fact they couldn't make it there
Or even make it to the air.
As if in a disappearing act
With conjuror, wand and hat,
By humankind's sleight of hand,
They'd vanished from their habitats.

And for the hosts the dinner date
Would be a long, long, long, long wait.

Poem sponsor:
Rajpoot Restaurant.
Thirty years serving fine Indian food.
www.rajpootrestaurantbristol.co.uk

Regift

It was my birthday yesterday.
One of the gifts, I have to say,
Was not my type or style or thing.
But kept in its original wrapping,
I gave it to my best friend Sue
For her dinner party do.
I didn't know she didn't like
Or that she gifted it to Mike
Who had one similar at home
So passed it on to mate Jerome.
He gave it not a second look
As it was not a comic book.
A leaving present it would make
For a party round at Jake's.
The design and colour didn't thrill
So Jake awarded it to Jill,
As a prize in a quiz game,
Yet her opinion was the same.
She took it round to neighbour Trace,
'Here's something for your brand new place.'
But Trace devised a thrifty plan:
To save it for her sister Fran.
And that was me - I have to say
I got it back on Christmas Day!
It must have saved folks lots of pounds
Doing the re-gifting rounds.

Poem sponsor:
Burton Sweet. Chartered Accountants and Business Advisors
www.burton-sweet.co.uk

Water Walk

At
one mile

I wish my day could
start like yours: on a

gentle walk to school, and
later to a shopping mall, a

party or a local park. At
two miles... I contemplate what

it's like at your place, to turn a
tap and see the flow of water for

a clean of teeth, a drink, a shower,
wash of clothes. At three miles...

I think of you, perhaps you're in
a swimming pool or eating at a

restaurant with water bottles
on your table. You ask and
then they're simply there.
At four miles... I ask myself
whether you ever give

an idle thought about my trek
through scorching heat to
the spring, the riverbank, a
muddy hole, where I collect
the dirty water I must drink.
I start the four mile journey
home... a full container on
my back. Sometimes I day-
dream about children in
other countries far away
from here, and wonder
what the distance is
of *their* daily
water walk.

WaterAid

Poem sponsor: **www.wateraid.org**
WaterAid's mission is to transform lives
by improving access to safe water,
hygiene and sanitation in the world's
poorest communities.

Gum

Stuck here, stuck there,
Around my mouth, in my hair,
Beneath my tongue and in my cheeks,
On my nose, my lips and teeth,
Between my fingers and my thumbs,
On my soles, my hands and bum,
On my back and on my tum,
Under desks, seats of chairs,
On my clothes, everywhere!
What's more, that squidgy chewing gum
Has stuck the toilet seat to mum!
The dog is gum-glued to the cat,
The hamster to a table mat.
What's worse is dad stares into space
Since I bubble-gummed his face.
Guess gooey gum is not his thing,
He never did look good in pink!
Gum can come in blobs and sticks,
Can lose its flavour in two licks,
Peppermint's the one for me
As long as it is sugar free.
Some will finger-twist and stretch,
If you swallow, make you wretch.
So as you chew the final chew,
Chew over something you can do:
Once your chewing session's done,
Remember it's not any fun
If a critter picks it up
And chokes on all that sticky stuff.
I know you won't be that gum dumb
So find a bin and dump the gum.

Poem sponsor: Mr. Ceri Owen-Roberts
Elgin Park Dental Practice www.elginpark.co.uk

Kendangered

White coated,
Arctic wanderer,
Ice traveller.

Silver-backed,
Ground-dweller,
Knuckle-walker.

Grey-skinned,
Megafauna,
Nose-horned.

These three poems are known as *Kennings*. Kennings
were written in Anglo-Saxon times. They are poems
which are like riddles. Can you guess which endangered
animal each poem is about? Then write your own!

Solar di da

The street says we're 'solar di da',
Without a doubt *green superstars*!
To make my point and show you proof,
We've solar panels on the roof.
The sun gods visit us most days
And flirt with our flat-plate arrays.

Ninety-three million miles away
Those sun gods barbie everyday.
They keep the sun in standby mode
And send the photons down our road.
Five billion years until it chills,
Until then you get no bills!

Perhaps it's really not that odd
That there were solar powered Gods
And all the ancient tribes now gone
Knew power could come from the sun.
Apollo, Sol, and Egypt's Ra –
To have such gods – so 'la di da'.

The sun god Ra was fit and hot,
He wooed girls with his solar yacht.
Apollo's 'find a goddess plan':
To sport his sun-blessed solar tan.
And Sol, third god of this triumvirate,
Spent all his time 'sun-dialling' dates.

Let's hope the sun gods will assist
With what's next on our shopping list:
We'd like a solar roller coaster
And a sun-run four slice toaster,
A *Bayliss* wind up radio,
That's 'solar di da' as well you know.

So...
Sun-drenched, sun-kissed
With solar cells,
We hope it's plain to see from far –
We are...
'Solar di da di da.'

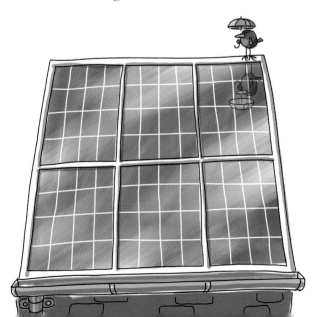

Trevor Bayliss OBE is the inventor of the wind-up
radio and a later model which is also solar powered.

Ghost Nets

Gill nets, purse nets, seine nets, trawl nets,
Ropes, floats, chains; lost or abandoned gear
Once used by fishermen.
Tonnes of monstrous mesh
Now fishing on its own:
Ghost nets.

And like the best of ghosts,
They often move around unseen,
Drifting with the ocean's current
Until a turtle, seabird, shark, dolphin or ray
Is tied in knots and twisted tangles.
Entrapped. Enwrapped.

Ensnared, they sink…
Taking other creatures
As they go…
Down and down…
Entombed, they decompose and disappear.

The empty ghost net floats back up
To the surface…
For another catch.

A Waste of Space

Paint flecks   cameras

toothbrush   wrench

pliers

circuit   boards   dead satellites

garbage bags

Space   debris   that   circled   the   Earth   .

Perhaps   that   procession   in   low   Earth   orbit

was   led by   the   glove

lost
by Ed White   on   his   first   spacewalk   .

A hand   that reminded   us

humans   created a   junkyard   in space   .

We   can   never   collect,   sweep up   or bin

what   we've   left   up there :

tens   of   thousands   of   orbiting   objects,

a   half   a   million

free

f   -   loa - ting   fr –   ag   –   ments,

m   i   l   l   i   o   n   s   of particles   of

space   scrap   collision   and   booster   explo -   sions .

What   a
waste
of

space   !

For Freya and Isaac Wilkinson.

21

Take Care Honey

'Take care honey. Be back by five,'
That's what I said as I waved him from the hive.
'Don't get eaten by a spider or a bug
Or captured by a kid who traps you in a mug.'

'Don't worry honey I'll get some food for us,
If I'm running late I'll give you a buzz.
I'll pick up the pollen and the nectar too,
I'll be back before you're done with all that worker stuff you do.'

The hours whiled by of my bee busy day,
He'd missed all the drama while he was away.
We'd all been stricken by a terrible disease,
The queen was dead and we bees were on our knees.

**I heard all about it from a passing drone,
But my navigation failed to find the route home.
Wings paralysed, I tumbled twice then spiralled round and round,
Everything went black as I dive-bombed to the ground.**

Little did I know he'd been poisoned on a plant,
But the news got back from a fast crawling ant.
He said pesticides or toxins made my honey breathe his last,
I was now the sole survivor of a colony collapse.

I had no idea it was our last goodbye
When I said 'take care honey' and waved him from the hive.
But 'take care honey' were the last words I said,
We'll soon be out of honey and *his honey* will be dead.

Poem sponsor: **Humble Bee Films** www.humblebeefilms.com
Humble Bee produces factual television focusing on nature, science and history.

Peakipedia

Mount Everest has the highest garbage dump in the world with a peak at 8,848 metres (29,029 ft) above sea level. Its expansive 'massif' or mountain group means there's plenty of space to dump stuff, especially things climbers don't want to carry to the summit, like empty gas bottles, tents, tent poles, climbing equipment, oxygen cylinders, utensils, fabric scraps, batteries, bottles, old socks, tin cans, cardboard, and all the trash left behind since Edmund Hillary and sherpa Tenzing Norgay first climbed Everest in 1953. Oops...forgot to mention the hundreds of kilos of poop. A lot of the rubbish is now visible thanks to disappearing glaciers and snow, due to global warming, which gives a nice trashy glow to the mountain's exterior. There's loads of room on the Everest massif so there should be plenty of room for a bit more junk if anyone has more they want to chuck. Remember Mount Everest is such a big mountain that perhaps it could all be buried inside. Then no one would notice it. The other names for Mount Everest are the Nepali *Sagarmāthā* which means 'Ocean mother', the Tibetan *Chomolungma* which means 'Goddess mother of the world', and *Mount Garbagejunka* which means 'giant bin god.'

Cold Comfort

Medically headedly,
Gwendoline Gordonstone
Went to the doctor and
Sneezed on his face.

Picked up her handkerchief -
Antibacterial -
Caught all the cold germs in
Cotton and lace.

This poem's form is known as a *Double Dactyl*. In Victorian times these poems were written as a game or for a bit of fun. A *dactyl* is a word with three syllables such as the word 'poetry'. A *double dactyl* is two three syllable words such as 'strawberry poetry'. So, how do you write a *double dactyl*?

The first line must be two 'nonsense words' of three syllables each. For example, *higgledy piggledy*. The second line must be a 3 + 3 syllables name of your poem's character. The third line must be 3 + 3 syllables and the fourth 3 + 1 syllables. The fifth line must be 3+3 syllables but the sixth line must be one single double dactyl word! That's a word with six syllables such as 'biodegradable'. The seventh line must be 3+3 syllables and the eighth line 3 + 1 syllables.

As if that isn't enough, your line 4 must rhyme with your line 8. Good luck with that! Here's another example where the rules have been changed a little. This time with the 6 syllable word in line five rather than line six.

Bean Drawing

Higgledy piggledy,
Dorothy Baltimore,
Writing her poetry,
Tried to be green.

Incomprehensibly,
Didn't use laptop or
Draw with a pencil but
Sketched with a bean.

Hare Raising News

WHAT is the reason that hares are still shot in their breeding season? Bright-eyed, long-eared, they hear the trigger pull. Long-legged they run – faster than a fox or you – but cannot win their race against the bullet.

The crime: they stole a beet or carrot – ate a tender shoot or two. Where's the law that bans the gun until their breeding is all done?

The gun is not the only thing the boxing hare would wish to knock out in the ring. How many leverets cannot flee oncoming farm machinery? Or the drove is run to ground illegally chased by courser's hounds. No-one knows how many die. How many end up in a pie?

I'd like to save these mad March hares. A century ago, four million leapt the land. Now eight hundred thousand still remain.

Their stories make hair-raising news, tales of woe, headlines of sorrow: hare today and gone tomorrow.

26

If My House Had No Toilet... What Would I Do?

If my house had no toilet what would I do?
Where would I go for a pee or a poo?
Out in the garden?
Out in the woods?
Or out in the fields with my bum in the mud?

If my school had no toilet what would I do?
Where would I fart if there weren't any loos?
Out in the playground?
In the school hall?
Wearing a nappy would be no good at all!

If my house had no taps what would I do?
How would we brew tea, boil eggs or make stew?
Where would I wash?
Where would I shower?
How would we water the houseplants and flowers?

If my school had no taps what would I do?
How would I clean hands sticky with glue?
How would I get paints
Off tables and chairs,
And the food from my lunchbox out of my hair?

With no toilets and taps I'd be like you,
Searching for somewhere to wash and to poo.
I'd drink dirty water
Found in a river,
That would upset my stomach and liver.

With toilets and taps you'd be like me,
With a great place to wash, shower, fart, poo and pee.
I'd like that to happen
As it's not right or fair,
That my house has two loos and you have nowhere.

For Zita.

Next Please

Patient:

Problems with my water, problems with my air,
Problem with my skin layers, sun-stripped bare.
Problem with my temperature so dangerously high,
Problems with my aches and quakes, can't think why.
Problem with intolerance to chemicals and grime,
I need a clean bill of health before I'm out of time.

Doctor:

Shall we try you on some pills?
Yet things have gone too far:
May be too late to operate
Or find another cure.
I see you're under lots of stress,
Perhaps you need a break?
Is there anyone to help you?
You've such a lot at stake.
I'd like to send you in for tests,
But what makes matters worse,
There isn't a hospital big enough to take planet Earth.

Light Romance

Don't squirm!
This beetle is actually called a worm.
The female doesn't fly but makes her mark
By glowing green in the dark.
Like a steady LED or remote in standby mode,
She can signal to a mate.
He's out late, flying by,
Spots her, comes down low and takes his chance.
That's how glow-worms date.
It's what might be called a 'light romance'.

In memory of Rachel (12th May 1989 - 18th May 2011)
Away from the noise and stress of the city, may glow-worms for ever light the path for us to find you.

Movie Melt

Was filming the ice cap when
as filming the ice cap whe
s filming the ice cap wh
filming the ice cap w
ilming the ice cap
lming the ice ca
ming the ice c
ing the ice
ng the ic
g the i
the
h

Poem sponsor: **The Pitch Project**
Pitch it ● Green it ● Film it ● Take it to Hollywood
www.enterthepitch.com

Frack Snack Recipe

This recipe makes a generous serving of natural gas with enough chemicals left over for a highly toxic side dish.

Utensils:
Hundreds of trucks, a deep well, drill pipe with drill bit, surface casing, blowout preventer, and a perforating gun bought from any local fracking store.

Preparation:
Line the well with concrete before adding ingredients.

Ingredients:
5,000,000 gallons of water.
40,000 gallons of chemicals. You can use any of the usual stuff: hydrochloric acid, hydrogen fluoride, diesel fuel, kerosene, methanol, benzene, xylene, polycyclic aromatic hydrocarbons.
A pinch of formaldehyde.

Method:
1. Drive trucks with supplies and water to and from fracking sites.
2. Pollute air on the way, raise noise levels and disturb wildlife.
3. Add 5,000,000 gallons of water.
4. Blend in the 40,000 gallons of chemicals.
5. Pour mixture into well under high pressure.
6. Allow shale rock at bottom to crack.
7. Wait until natural gas is released and serve up with a side dish of leftover chemicals.
8. Leave non-biodegradable chemicals to evaporate and create contaminated air, acid rain and ground level ozone.
9. Experience sensory, respiratory and neurological damage.
10. Recipe for disaster?

Litter Twit

My friend Jasmine Shaw
Isn't green anymore.
Can't be bothered to pick up her litter,
She'd rather spend time on Facebook and Twitter.

This type of poem was invented by Edmund Clerihew Bentley (1875-1956) when he was sixteen years old! It's called a *Clerihew*! Can you guess why? A Clerihew has simple rules: it is four lines long; the first line has to have the name of a person; the first and second lines must rhyme and so must the third and fourth. But most of all, the poem must be funny!

The Green and Non-green List of Collective Nouns

A hooarray of solar panels.
A whooshwhirl of wind turbines.
A compostation of organic farmers.
A posy of environmentalists.
A looploop of recyclers.
A chuff of conservationists.
A spinachorium of health food delis.
A canopycopia of treehuggers.
A bucket of charity workers.

A slickerate of oil polluters.
A carbonnetory of car commuters.
A rubbishery of fly-tippers.
A dumbduff of deforesters.
A litter of litterers.
A naughtynought of greedy bankers.
A higheyesorery of landfillers.
A predation of poachers.
A trolley of shopperholics.

Nurse-a-tree Rhyme

Rock-a-bye baby in the tree tops.
When the wind blows
The cradle will rock.
When the bough breaks
The cradle will fall,
Down will come baby, cradle and all.

Rock-a-bye-baby in the tree tops.
When slash and burn comes,
Soya exports,
Expansion of crops,
The cradle will rock.
As the wind of greed blows,
Boughs break, cradle falls,
Down will come baby, cradle and all.
Up will go C02 gases and all.

Rock-a-bye-baby in the tree tops.
When earthmovers roll in
For highways and roads
And urban sprawl sprawls,
The cradle will rock.
As construction shakes roots,
Boughs break, cradle falls,
Down will come baby, cradle and all.
Down come indigenous people and all.

Rock-a-bye baby in the tree tops.
When the mangroves are drained
And cleared for shrimp farms
Or plundered for oil,
The cradle will rock.
As mining takes place,
Boughs break, cradle falls,
Down will come baby, cradle and all.
Down will come villages, hamlets and all.

Rock-a-bye baby in the tree tops.
When cattle is reared
For meat for cafés
And beefburger buns,
The cradle will rock.
When guts demand food,
Boughs break, cradle falls,
Down will come baby, bark, branches and all.
Down will come habitats, wildlife and all.

Rock-a-bye baby in the tree tops.
When the wind blows
The cradle will rock.
When the bough breaks,
They'll see they are wrong
As they're cutting the branch they're all sitting upon.

Green Pirate G-arrr-gs

What did the green pirate say?
Shiver me responsibly sourced timbers!

Why wouldn't the green pirate walk the plank?
It didn't meet EU Timber regulations.

Why didn't the green pirate bury his treasure?
He didn't want to contribute to landfill.

Why was the green pirate good at singing long sea shanties?
He had sustain ability.

Why did the green pirate say rrra?
He'd recycled an arrr!

What's a green pirate's favourite source of power?
Solarrr energy.

Which movie did the vegetable loving green pirate
want to star in?
Pirates of the CarrotBean.

For Bruno, Rafaela and Wilf Wilkinson.

Planet Poo

In a fart away galaxy…
Is a planet made of poo,
Its bleak terrain is black and brown
With lighter patches too.

It's in *Constipalation Laxivity*,
A distant constellation,
But how the planet came to be
Provokes much conversation.
(Like whose original poo was it anyway?)

Some think it was a single poo
That inflated as it grew,
Others say that it expanded
From big bangs in someone's loo.

The planet's weather?
Windy gusts with showers of yellow rain
Which the alien poopeeps process
With the sewage in their drains.

The slippery sludgey mess they make,
Supplies the planet's power.
Their one-stop energy advice:
Use the toilet twice an hour.

The poo-crews shovel poo all day
Until the end of business bell.
If the poo piles reach their armpits,
They know the dig went well.

When the final mound of steaming poo
Glistens in the setting sun,
The poopeeps rest their weary heads,
They're glad the day's work's dung!

Poem sponsor: Proud to be partnered with **Bristol, European Green Capital 2015**.
www.bristol2015.co.uk

The Ballad of the Freshwater Pearl Mussel

At the Ennerdale Water in Cumbria
Where the lake meets the River Ehne's flow,
A colony of molluscs was born on the bed
Almost two centuries ago.

Known as the freshwater pearl mussel,
These molluscs can fashion a pearl.
You might guess that these are well fancied
By a gem-loving boy or a girl.

Have you heard of the 'river bank robbers'
And the illegal pearl fishing they do?
How they poach for the innocent mussel,
It's a story that isn't so new.

The Roman invasion of Britain,
In the year fifty-five BC,
Wasn't only to plunder the mineral wealth,
But to gather more pearl jewellery.

Onwards to the twelfth century,
Scotland's first King did the same.
Alexander would boast to his subjects,
'No man has more pearls to his name.'

Since then it's not been much different,
As the waters watched over the years
How the mussels were ruthlessly murdered
And riverbed homes disappeared.

It's a cold heartless crime to take them.
Imagine the loss down the line.
They'd easily live over one hundred years,
If not cut down in their prime.

Yet the mussel's decline and its downfall
Isn't only determined by theft,
Engineering, pollution, construction of weirs,
Have dictated how many are left.

Did you hear of the colony's tragedy?
Eighty thousand wiped out in one go
In two thousand and twelve at Ennerdale
Where the lake meets the River Ehne's flow.

Their water, habitat, oxygen,
Were disrupted by I wonder who?
Individuals, corporate companies,
Or was it a mix of the two?

That's the end of my tale about Ennerdale,
So I'll close with a word of advice:
Protect the freshwater pearl mussel,
And endeavour to save this pearl of great price.

For Maggie.

Sweet (W)Rapper

Bust this rhyme - can you dig da scene?
Was hawkin' out da hood
When a drop cruised by,
In foe deep wiv a dukey roped stunna
Phat pumpin' out da bass,
Freestylin' with da flow of da MC man,
Kickin' it live on da gas wiv his Timbs,
Tagged fly hoodie hood blowin' in da wind,
Bling-blinged hand hangin' out da whip,
Tappin'out da jam with da fingertips,
Other hand's in a box of candy treats,
Poppin' choc drops to da eat me beat,
Spittin' sweet wrappers high into da air,
Dissing da environment like he don't care,
Flamboastin' flaker not using his bean,
Sketchy rapper's wrappers hit a fed's windscreen.
Cross fade da rhyme to...
Berry flashing beams
As he breaks a buck fifty away from da scene,
But Five-0 swervers still chasin' his ride,
Force da Benz over, hop on da side,
Check out da peeps on da litter buggin' trip,
Don't take da gasface da front or da dap,
Give da boyz their own slammin' popo rap,
'Yo cats are played out and lunchin' around,
What's goin wi' yo wrapper trash lying on da ground?
Pull up yo saggin' pants hangin' off yo bum,
Heavy wiv choc bars, chews, mints, gums,
Why're yo dudes so rapper wrapper dumb?
Pick 'em all up or da crew get booked,
Rhyme that one at da lab on your next track cut!'

Vocabulary:

Berry - police car
Bling bling - jewellery
Break - move quickly
Buggin' - acting weird or strange
Bust this - to pay attention, listen to this
Buck fifty - a fast getaway
Benz - Mercedes Benz car
Can you dig it - can you understand
Cats - people
Cut - a record music track
Dap - a high five
Dissing - disrespect
Drop - convertible car
Dudes - group of people usually guys
Dukey rope - a thick gold chain
Flamboastin' - flamboyant and boasting
Five-0 - police car
Flaker - unreliable or lazy person
Fly - attractive
Freestyle - improvise a rhyme to a beat
Front - put on a false impression
Gasface - give someone a stupid look
Hawk - look at something
Hop on the side - to get in a car
In foe deep - a car with four people in it
Jam - music or a music track
Lab - recording studio
Lunchin' - behaving erratically
MC - Master of Ceremonies or Microphone Controller
Phat - a good rap attiude
Popo - police
Sketchy - shady
Stunna - wealthy person
Swerver - car

For Luka.

Elastic Plastic?

This
is a
poem
about
bottles.
It really is
drastic that
those made
of plastic
once full of
spring water
end up in a
dump. To
u s e t h e m
again, would
be fantastic!
Could they
spring back
as if on elastic?

Flower Power!

Wild flowers are wild man! Kinda wild!
They're the hippies of flowering communes:
Blow your mind blossoms, mellowed out shrubs
Who know how to chill out and get a good vibe.
No one tells *them* where to go... where to grow.
They're not uncool like those planted in rows,
They're far out fest flowers not ones to be cut and arranged for the shows!

Wild flowers are wild man! Kinda wild!
Their seeds blag a ride on the back of the wind
Or hitch a lift on the legs of a bee,
Inside a bird or stick to the wool of a wandering sheep.
Until they're dropped off...
Somewhere they never expected to be (where it's at man!)
To crash pad on coastlines, hedgerows and woodland, marshes and meadows,
It's hip that they know where to groovily grow!

Wild flowers are wild man! Kinda wild!
Outasight happenings, way out there flora,
Funky and free-living friends of the Earth,
A tie-dye of crimson, pink, yellow, blue, purple,
Linked petal to petal in silent protest:
'Leave us in peace! Don't trample or pick. We're wilder than wild.
We're flowers of power that go with the flow,
Get it together - we do our own thing -
We dig flower power that's all you should know!'

For Freda, Isla and Ava Cory.

Feel Good Poem

Scrawl the first line with your toe in the sand,

The second you write on the wind with your hands,

Sing out ten syllables for a line three,

INVISIBLY TRACE LINE FOUR ON A TREE.

Snow-scribe a fifth with iced finger tip,

Draw a few more in the mud with a stick,

Now a few couplets signed out in the air,

Embroider another on something you wear.

Spell out a sentence with shells on the shore,

Go decorate cakes with three nouns or more,

Secretly circle-cut lines in a crop,

Blow ten words in dust and add a full stop.

Complete the stanza in surf-swirling waves,

Shout the end rhyme in an echoey cave.

Poem sponsor: Paul Burden at **PerformWell Performance Coaching**
www.performwell.co.uk

No More Passengers

Two centuries ago America's skies
Had billions of birds on the wing.
The commonest by far of all of them
Was the Passenger Pigeon.

The Passengers flew in the densest of flocks,
But it made them a sure-fire target
For hunters to net or shoot down for feathers
And cheap meat to sell at the market.

It wasn't too long before habitats fell
To clear land for farms and new towns.
With no laws to protect the Passengers,
Their numbers plummeted down.

Only then did the government lend an ear
To prevent any hunt near a nest,
But the plight of the species was only too clear –
Too little too late – few pigeons were left.

So the Union of Ornithologists
Offered a handsome reward
To anyone finding a colony,
Yet no-one ever collected that hoard.

Can you believe that by nineteen-hundred,
The birds had almost all gone?
Then a boy in Ohio went into the wild
And killed the very last one.

It was Chicago's Professor Whitman
Who held on to a pigeon or two.
He sent the last pair of Passengers
To Cincinnati Zoo.

The zoo had a pigeon called Martha
It was hoped she'd choose one of the males,
But they died leaving Martha alone again
As all mating attempts failed.

Martha, the last Passenger Pigeon,
Aged twenty-nine, died alone
On September the First, nineteen-fourteen,
At one in the afternoon.

Extinction means gone forever.
It's absurd to let it occur.
Seems impossible to go from billions to none
And end up with no Passengers.

"Would like to meet...
for fun, friendship and
possibly marriage.
Will travel..."

Alien Postcard

To. Mrs. Squadge Alien
876 Volcano View Terrace
Craterville
Somulus 3
Universe UN1 END

Hi Mum,

Finally got here after a three trillion light
year journey with only one stop for a pee at
Alpha Centauri three. Ouch - was desperate
to go.

Earth is a cool place, well it's getting hotter actually,
but Earthlings keep arguing about whether it's getting
hotter or not.

Went for a swim yesterday. They've got a massive
pool of melting ice up by the Arctic and all that
rushing water kept pulling my trunks down.
(Got a cold bum!) PS. with icicles.

Tomorrow going to see some islands which might
disappear soon so will send you a photo before they
do. There's a lot of rubbish here; some people live on it,
some people bury it and some recycle it like we do.

It's a sick place. That's sick as in good !
It'll be interesting to see if they can keep it that
way for my next holiday.
But not sure I'll book with Global Warming Travel again.

Al x

For Sam, Lucy and Caspar McKinlay.

Ovation

If every part of every nation
Had squeaky clean safe sanitation
With water set free from stagnation,
Then in all the loos in world locations
There'd be applause and celebration.
(As long as there's no constipation!)
Seat lids would rise with grand elation
To shouts and cheers of acclamation,
(At least for thirty days duration)
From rich, poor, stranger, friend, relation,
And all involved in poo creation
At houses, shops, cafés, train stations,
Where toilet paper declarations
Prompt them with the information:
'Please sit or stand for an ovation
Given to this recitation:
Squeaky clean safe sanitation
For every part of every nation.'

Balcony Scene

Enter Romeo.

Romeo: All in darkness at the Capulets' house…
Except for a first floor bedroom window.
Balcony lights have been left on again!
Why does my Juliet waste energy?

What is it that she now so softly speaks
As she selects 'cottons' on the tumble?
I'd counsel her to hang her washing out
Where night's sweet scented air dries it for free.

I hear her speak…

Juliet: Romeo where are you?
Will you deny the hue of Montague
That eco-green, my family's enemy?
Be some other: purple, blue. That would do.

R: Shall I speak? Better keep green lips well zipped.

J: My father owns the Capulets' landfill,
And yours the Montague recycling plant.
Environmentally, we are mismatched.
So if you cannot choose to change your cause,
Swear you love me and I will dump my own.

R: Perhaps for my love I should give up greens
And all my charitable subscriptions
To sites and charities that save the Earth.
No more newsletters or email alerts.
I'll recycle my aims, perhaps my name,
And be no longer eco-Romeo.
Too bad, I liked that name. She's spotted me!

J: Who's hiding down there listening in on me?
R: The guy who does your bins. Can't say my name.
J: How did you dodge the CCTV cams?
R: Love lifted me above your garden scrap.

J: Watch out! The Capulet guards will get you!
R: In their heavy armour they'll not gain ground.
They'll swelter by the heat of climate change.
I know you think that science is all wrong,
But it's true my love. See. I'm in my shorts!
With boundless energy let's swear true love -
Sustainable love - with compromises!

J: Let me switch off this light that troubles you.
I'll swear to my love in the moon's soft glow
And promise I will use fewer gadgets.
Pray let me keep my three speed hairdryer.
R: I too will swear true love my Juliet
By any lamp or light you might leave on
As long as it is energy saving.
J: Then, if your purpose truly is marriage,
Ping me a text about the date and time.

Call from within from Energy Inspector.

EI: I've come to read your meter.

For Serafina.

Stag Sonnet

The Exmoor Emperor has been shot dead.
Too long he stood proud in a rifle's sight.
Cold trophy hunters sought his noble head.
They paid blood money for the shooting rights.

Now fully bled and lifeless lies the deer
Whose age-old genes will not be passed around.
He did not get his chance to rut this year.
Majesty and power are run to ground.

His ghost will wander in the wilderness
And grace the forests that the stag once roamed.
Where is the body? Anyone might guess.
His antlers now adorn a stately home.

I am still staggered by the news report
That killing can be such a thrilling sport.

In October 2010 a giant red stag known as the 'Exmoor Emperor',
thought to have been the biggest animal in the UK, was shot by
a hunter on Exmoor. The stag was still in its mating season.

Fashion Ration

My wardrobe is bursting,
The shelves crammed and bulging,
Drawers are chock full to the brim.
I wish I could ration
My passion for fashion
But I love wearing stuff that is 'in'.

Most of the gear
On the hangers in here
Are skirts that have hardly been worn.
Outfits are demoted
If they're not noticed
When I'm out dancing till dawn.

I don't give a thought
To the last dress I bought,
It looked good on display at the store.
Got worn for a week,
It's no longer chic,
The colourway's now such a bore.

I have fifty pairs
Of shoes I don't wear
Piled in a heap on the floor.
The heels I wore twice,
The platforms too high,
The stilettos caused blisters and sores.

My new trainers were great,
But now they get hate,
Since the logo's design got an update.
How can I ration
This craving for fashion?
I love wearing labels I rate.

I could customise
My jeans from full size,
And cut off the legs to make shorts.
Then rip or edge fray
The denim away
And add a front flap for a skort.

I'll go buy a classic
Trans-seasonal jacket,
To wear from autumn to spring.
I won't wash my clothes
On daily half loads
And expand the life of my things.

Instead of buy new
Better mend or make do,
Why be a cool fashionista?
I'll charity shop
For all of my tops
And become a recessionista.

My wardrobe is bursting,
The shelves crammed and bulging,
Drawers are chock full to the brim.
But I've resolved to ration
My passion for fashion
And wear out my stuff that is 'in'.

Poem Sponsor: **Otrovez**. Creative Cross-Media,
www.otrovez.com

Hymnerick

A green organist Harry McGrue,
Played a church organ powered from poo,
When selecting a hymn
For the congregation to sing,
He always chose *Allelu – loo*!

Roundelay for Rag-pickers

Here's something about recycling
That's not a good link in the chain:
The slum kids who rag-pick the bins
And rummage on landfill terrains.
Rag-pickers earn hardly a thing
From the rubbish their sacks contain.

The slum kids who rag-pick the bins
And rummage on landfill terrains,
They scavenge cans, bottles and tins,
But a doubt in their brain remains:
Rag-pickers earn hardly a thing
From the rubbish their sacks contain.

They scavenge cans, bottles and tins,
But a doubt in their brain remains:
The junk sold to bring money in,
Makes not enough cash to sustain.
Rag-pickers earn hardly a thing
From the rubbish their sacks contain.

The junk sold to bring money in,
Makes not enough cash to sustain.
Even life-long landfill climbing
Would not stop the constant refrain:
Rag-pickers earn hardly a thing
From the rubbish their sacks contain.

Go on – drive yourself mad writing a *Roundelay*.
The Roundelay has 24 lines set out in four stanzas of six lines each.
The twelve pairs of lines in the poem are arranged in this pattern: ABR/BCR/CDR/DER.
R is the two-line refrain that ends each stanza. There are eight syllables to a line.

Houseplant Rant

I didn't get watered today.
Have you flown to your villa in Spain?
I'm stuck home alone on a tray.
I didn't get watered today.
No flamencos for me or olés
As my leaves start their wilt and their wane.
I didn't get watered today.
Have you flown to your villa in Spain?

This poem is a *Triolet*. A Triolet stems from medieval French poetry and is a poem with eight lines. Its rhyme scheme is *ABaAabAB*. The first, fourth and seventh lines are identical, as are the second and final lines, which make the first and final couplets identical.

Poem sponsor: **Richard Harding Estate Agents**.
www.richardharding.co.uk

Talking Rubbish

'...he was talking a load of rubbish.'

'Yeah? What did he say?'

'He said he was going to dump me.'

'Dump you? Where?'

'The dump I guess.'

'What a waste! Hey, don't cry Trashy.'

'It's Tracy.'

'Sorry. Tracy. Don't cry.'

'Can't help it. Keep thinking back to when I first met him on the landfill. I was chilling out on a pile of plastic and he was floating down from the sky as if he'd been sent down from heaven.'

'Probably got chucked from up there!'

'Do you really think so Debris?'

'It's Debbie.'

'Sorry, Debbie. And then he sent me that love litter.'

'Bin it. Look, he's just a piece of scrap that got dropped by a random seagull. And you, you're really a lovely, heartwarming, funny and friendly great piece of junk.'

'Really?'

'Yeah really. But s'pose at the very least he could have offered to recycle you.'

Green Sounds FM Radio

Green Sounds Radio has an all night spot,
Presented by a long-eared bat and an ocelot.
Tawny owl is engineer on the station's show,
Gives the five four three two hoot… programme ready to go!
Fades in whistles of the wind sweeping sea and shore,
Mixes to the scamper of a mouse across a floor.
Right channel is a thrush with a serenading tweet,
Left channel has a gossiping parakeet.
Crossfades to the drama of a thunderstorm,
Turns up the level of a locust swarm.
Pans right to the trickle of a woodland stream,
Pans left to a geyser spraying out steam.
Stereo centres on the buzz of a bee,
With the ambient flutter of leaves in a tree.
Blends in forest fire on the audio track,
Adds a backing loop of a mallard's quack.
Peaks at the crunch of the Earth's tectonic plates,
Pumps up the bass as the ground vibrates.
Tawny checks the clock at one fifteen,
Fades out with a lion's roar to end the scene.
Then a 'green goodnight and that's your lot.'
From the long-eared bat and the ocelot.

Dedicated to Edward Williams (1921-2013) composer and inventor of the Soundbeam.
www.soundbeam.co.uk

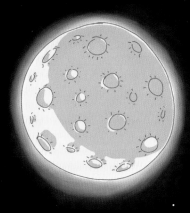

Planet Nonet

Astronauts on the lunar surface,
Contemplated the Earth from space.
Our precious world is fragile,
Wars and squabbles futile,
Small blue marbled ball,
One place for all.
Comprehend?
Befriend,
Mend.

Here's a *Nonet*. Quite a brain challenge to write! Start a line
with nine syllables and write each successive line with one
less syllable until you get down to one! Make the lines
rhyme if you want an extra challenge!

Transformers

You've seen it in a comic,
You've seen it on TV,
You've seen it on the Internet,
And now in poetry!
The theme is superheroes,
But not the movie kind,
That POW! ZOOM! BAM! and clean up
The city's streets of crime.

The superheroes that I saw
Keep their profile low,
We might walk past them unawares
As invisibly they go.
They have no armour, weapons,
Or any special power,
These humble warriors tread the streets
With a shovel, brush and barrow.
Their mission: binning coffee cups, bottles, bags and trays,
Any piece of garbage dumped throughout the day.

I passed them on the highway,
They had yellow baseball caps
With the word TRANSFORMERS
Emblazoned on the back.

It's true we like the movies and the heroes that we see,
But I saw the *real* transformers
Who clean up the *real* streets.

Visual Pollution

A sign cuts off a hillside view
With the message 'fones for u.'
Banners criss-cross harbour scenes
Promoting 'two for one' cuisine.
Pavement signs for bars and pubs
Block bushes, plants, wildflowers, shrubs.
Still larger boards boast fish 'n' chips,
But hide the coastline, sea and ships.
Even avenues of trees
Compete with advertising tease,
And billboards scrolling movie dramas
Steal the place of panoramas.
How much hard sell do we need
On the highways and the streets?
This is no marketing solution,
It's corporate visual pollution.

Poem sponsor: **Juul and Payne, Advanced Eyecare**.
www.juulandpayne.co.uk.

Articulate

He opened the door.
Drip
Drip
Drip
The freezer had failed.
Ice in the trays was melting away.
Drip
Food he had frozen was all going off.
Drip
Drip
He'd phone the manufacturers and make a complaint!
He'd articulate what had gone wrong.
Then as
Drip
Drip
Gush...
The water flooded the floor,
It prompted a thought:
The same thing was happening
Not in a freezer but on planet Earth.
Should he be freezer articulating?
Or polar ice cap *Arctic*ulating?
What's more important -
The freezer drip dripping under his nose
Or the North Pole so many miles away?
It's something he sees on the Net now and then,
But the polar ice melt doesn't mean much to him.
Well not...
Until...
There's no ice to reflect sunlight back to space,
The Earth's cooling system has finally gone,
Polar bears can't get to the ice for their hunts,
Ice free seasons become excessively long.
So, should he freezer articulate?
Drip
Drip
Drip
Or polar ice cap *Arctic*ulate? Or is it *Arctic*toolate?
Too late!
Gushhhhhhhhhhhhhhhhhhhhhhhhhhhhhhhhhhhhhhhhhhhhhhhhhhh!

Health Food Nut

In macrobiotic yoghurt,
I shower, bathe, scrub and shampoo,
I get my hair dry then plait it with herbs
Or pods of fresh mangetout.

I knitted a jumper with bean shoots
To match gluten free spaghetti socks.
I've got shoes with platform soled tofu
And a vegan stir-fried noodle frock.

I crocheted a hat out of wheatgrass
And lined it with raw sauerkraut.
My pants are a patchwork of spinach
Cross stitched with alfalfa sprouts.

I braided a skirt with spring onions,
Made a garlic clove belt for the waist,
It had sequins of forest fruit muesli
With organic food bars interlaced.

I know it seems crazy to others
That I dress in what's good for my gut,
But I can't think of anything better
Than being a health food nut.

Poem sponsor:
Wild Oats
Natural Foods Bristol.
Celebrating natural, organic
and fairtrade living.
www.wild-oats.co.uk

Please Don't Sneeze

There's a new species in a land afar,
Discovered in the mountains of Myanmar.
It's the snub-nosed monkey with a turned up nose
And a very clever somnolent seated pose.
Head between legs, he endeavours to stop
His nostrils being tickled by water drops.
Otherwise hunters will spot him in the trees,
By waiting for the rain and the primate's sneeze!
Endangered sneezing monkey don't achoo please,
Keep your head firmly hidden in-between your knees!

Wordworthy World

Fantasmagorical,
Superincredible,
Wowfabsuperical,
Splendifermarvellous,
Ultraremarkable,
Brilltastigorical,
Gloriphenomenous,
Senswickedational,
Wondermazezoriful,
Coolterrifantical,
Inspirastonishing,
Awesotremenderous,
Extraordibewildernary,
Specstupentacular,
Life giving,
Wordworthy
Beautiful Earth.

Dedicated to Jonathon Porritt and his book
The World We Made (Alex McKay's Story from 2050)
www.forumforthefuture.org

www.martinkiszko.com
www.greenpoemsforablueplanet.com